**1** (10)

**2** (10)

**3**    C melodic minor (10)

A♭ major

E major

F# harmonic minor

**4**    D flat        E / E natural        B / B natural (10)

A flat        F sharp        D / D natural

**5** (10)

**8**
(10)

**Andante** means:
- at a medium speed ✔
- quick
- slow
- in a singing style

**Tempo comodo** means:
- with some freedom of time
- at a comfortable speed ✔
- in time
- first time

**Largamente** means:
- broadly ✔
- sad, sorrowful
- light
- majestic

**a tempo** means:
- in time ✔
- held back
- the end
- a little

**sf** means:
- *staccatissimo*
- slight pressure
- moderately loud
- forced, accented ✔

**:‖** means:
- the end
- bar-line
- repeat mark ✔
- double bar-line

**9** (a)
(10)

(i)   7th

(ii)  F♯ minor

(iii) simple quadruple

(iv)  false

(v)

(b)
(10)

# Theory Paper  Grade 3  2019  B
## Model Answers

**1** (10)

**2** (10)

**3** (10)

(a)

(b)

**4**   A major   G minor   C♯ minor   (10)

   D minor   E major

**5** (10)

**6** (10)

**7** (10)

**8** (10)

**Adagio** means:

at a medium speed ☐

quick ☐

slow ☑

fairly quick ☐

*ad libitum* means:

in the style of ☐

in the same way ☐

becoming more lively ☐

at choice ☑

*deciso* means:

emphatic, accented ☐

energetic ☐

with determination ☑

delicate ☐

◌ means:

strong accent ☐

slight pressure ☑

*staccatissimo* ☐

*staccato* ☐

*con brio* means:

with love ☐

with some freedom of time ☐

with vigour, lively ☑

with a minim beat ☐

*da capo* (*D.C.*) means:

repeat from the sign ☐

repeat from the beginning ☑

the end ☐

in time ☐

**9** (a) (10)

    (i)   true

           true

    (ii)  six

    (iii) D

    (iv) two / two crotchets / two quarter notes / one minim / one half note / one beat

(b) (10)

# Theory Paper   Grade 3   2019   C
## Model Answers

**1** (10)

etc.

etc.

etc.

**2** (10)

(a)

(b)

*or*

*or*

**3**   major      perfect      major      (10)
      6th    octave / 8ve / 8th    7th

            minor        major
            3rd          2nd

**4**   C sharp    G / G natural    G flat    (10)

   F / F natural    D sharp    A / A natural

**5** (10)

**6** (10)

**7** (10)

**8** (10)

| **Allegro** means: | | *Fine* means | | *leggiero* means: | |
|---|---|---|---|---|---|
| at a medium speed | ☐ | a little | ☐ | graceful | ☐ |
| quick | ✔ | in time | ☐ | smoothly | ☐ |
| fairly quick | ☐ | the end | ✔ | heavy | ☐ |
| slow | ☐ | repeat from the beginning | ☐ | light | ✔ |

| *tenuto* means: | | *fp* means: | | *con moto* means: | |
|---|---|---|---|---|---|
| held | ✔ | loud, gradually getting quieter | ☐ | with movement | ✔ |
| too much | ☐ | loud, then immediately quiet | ✔ | more movement | ☐ |
| slow | ☐ | quiet, gradually getting louder | ☐ | less movement | ☐ |
| speed, time | ☐ | quiet, then immediately loud | ☐ | without movement | ☐ |

**9** (a) (10)

   (i)   C minor

   (ii)  false

   (iii)  Bar 8

   (iv)  five

   (v)  *legato* (smoothly)

  (b) (10)

# Theory Paper    Grade 3    2019    S
## Model Answers

**1**                                                                                      (10)

**2**                                                                                      (10)

**3**                                                                                      (10)

**4**                                                                                      (10)

**5**    perfect            minor            major                                          (10)
    5th                7th                2nd

       perfect            major
   octave / 8ve / 8th        6th

**6** (10)

**7** (10)

**8** (10)

| ***p*** means: | | **stringendo** means: | | *dolce* means: | |
|---|---|---|---|---|---|
| quiet | ✔ | gradually getting louder | ☐ | playful | ☐ |
| very quiet | ☐ | gradually getting quieter | ☐ | sweet | ✔ |
| moderately quiet | ☐ | gradually getting slower | ☐ | stately | ☐ |
| loud | ☐ | gradually getting faster | ✔ | merry | ☐ |

| *subito* means: | | ⌢ means: | | **non troppo** means: | |
|---|---|---|---|---|---|
| simple, plain | ☐ | pause on the note or rest | ✔ | very much | ☐ |
| always | ☐ | perform the notes smoothly | ☐ | too much | ☐ |
| suddenly | ✔ | *staccato*: detached | ☐ | not too much | ✔ |
| sustained | ☐ | accent the note | ☐ | not in time | ☐ |

**9 (a)** (10)

    (i)   compound

          duple

    (ii)  7th

    (iii) D major

    (iv) four

    (v)  Bars 5 and 6

  (b) (10)